COWBOY SAM AND BIG BILL
COWBOY SAM
COWBOY SAM AND FREDDY
COWBOY SAM AND THE RODEO
COWBOY SAM AND THE RUSTLERS

COWBOY SAM AND PORKY
COWBOY SAM AND SHORTY
COWBOY SAM AND THE FAIR
COWBOY SAM AND THE INDIANS

COWBOY SAM AND DANDY
COWBOY SAM AND MISS LILY
COWBOY SAM AND FLOP
COWBOY SAM AND SALLY
COWBOY SAM AND THE AIRPLANE

Cowboy

pictures by Jack Merryweather

Sam and Big Bill

by Edna Walker Chandler

BENEFIC PRESS • CHICAGO

PUBLISHING DIVISION OF BECKLEY-CARDY COMPANY

STORIES

Library of Congress
Number 60-8888

Big Bill Comes to the Ranch

Here is Cowboy Sam.

Here is Shorty.

Here is Sam's ranch.

Sam and Shorty work on the ranch.

They work with the cows.

Cowboys help Sam and Shorty.
The cowboys like to work.
They are happy on Sam's ranch.

One day Big Bill came.

He saw Cowboy Sam.

Big Bill said, "I want to work.

I like it here.

I want to work on the ranch."

Sam said, "We work here.
We work with cows.
We like all the ranch work.
We like to eat, too.
We like to eat good things.
Can you make good things to eat?"

Bill said, "I can make
one good thing to eat.
I will make it for you."

Big Bill made something good.
Cowboy Sam liked what he made.
Shorty liked what he made.
Freckles liked it, too.

Here is what Bill made.

He made it that day.

He made it again.

He made it over and over.

Big Bill Wants Help

One day Sam said to Big Bill,
"We like what you have made.
But we want something new.
Can you make something new?"

Big Bill was not happy.

Sam wanted something new to eat.

So did Shorty.

Freckles wanted something new, too.

They did not eat what Bill made.

Big Bill wanted help.
He looked and looked.
He saw something.
"I will get it," he said.
"It will help."

Bill worked
and worked.
He made new
things to eat.

"Now we like what
you make," Sam said.
"We like all the
things you make."

What Will Bill Make?

One day Bill saw something.
"What fun!" he said to Sam.
"We will go," Sam said.
"We will all go there."

"We can take things to eat.
They will be good things," said Bill.
"I will make a surprise.
We will take it to eat."

Bill worked and worked.

He did not want Sam to see.

He did not want Shorty to see.

"Go away!" he said.

"It is a surprise!"

"The surprise will go here," Bill said.

"You can not have it, Freckles.

You can not have the surprise."

Sam and Shorty went to sleep.

Big Bill went to sleep.

Freckles went to sleep, too.

But something did not go to sleep!

Now Freckles was not sleeping.
He saw something!
He went after what he saw.
Down came the surprise!

Now Big Bill was not sleeping.
He came to see.
He did not like what he saw.
The surprise had come down.
"Freckles, you did this!" he said.
"Go away!
Go away!"

Big Bill looked and looked.

It was not a good surprise now.

"I will make a new surprise.

I have to do it again," he said.

Big Bill went to work again.

He worked and worked.

He made a new surprise.

Sam and Shorty came to Bill.
They wanted to see what Bill made.
"Go away!" Bill said.
"Go away, Sam and Shorty!
You can not see the surprise."

"Bill is funny.
He likes to make
things," said Sam.
"He works all day.
He works at night.
Funny Bill!"

The Day for Fun

Sam said, "The day for fun is here.
We will eat now.
Then we will have to work.
After work, we will all go away."

Sam and Shorty did the ranch work.

Big Bill worked too.

He worked with the surprise.

Freckles did not work.

"Now we will go," Sam said.

"Good," said Bill.

"Will we take the surprise?
Will it go with us?" said Bill.

"The surprise will go," said Shorty.

"We will take it."

"Good!" said Sam.
"We will have fun.
Here we go!"

Shorty saw something.
"Look!" he said.
"We will have fun."

"We will see the cows," said Sam.
"There will be good cows here."
Shorty was happy.
"I want to see the cows," he said.
"I do, too," said Sam.

Sam and Shorty saw the cows.
They looked and looked.
"Look, Bill," said Sam.
"Here is a good cow."

Where Is Bill?

Big Bill was not there.
"Did Bill go away?" said Sam.

"Come, Shorty," said Sam.
"We will look for Bill.
We want to find Big Bill."

They looked and
looked for Bill.
They looked here . . .

They looked there . .
They did not find.
Big Bill.

"We will get something to eat.
We will go now," said Sam.
"We can look for Bill there.
He likes good things to eat."

Then Sam saw Bill.

"We looked for you," said Sam.

"But we did not find you!

Here you are!"

Bill's Surprise

Big Bill said, "I worked.
I made a good surprise.
Then I made it again.
You will like the good surprise."

A man said, "Here it is.
Here is the one we like.
Come here, Big Bill."

Big Bill went to the man.

He was happy.

Sam was happy.

Shorty was happy, too.

The man came to Big Bill.
"Good for you!" he said.
"You can make good things to eat!"

"What a surprise!" said Sam.
"We can not eat the surprise now.
We will get something to eat.
But it will not be the surprise."

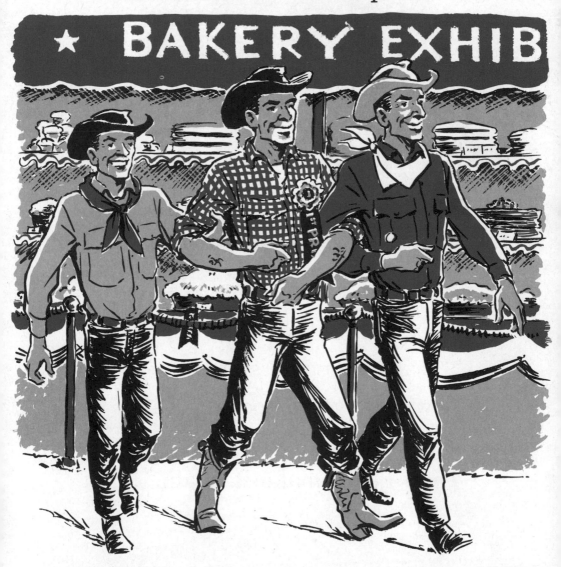

"I can make new things now.
They will be good," said Bill.
"I will make the surprise for you.
It will be good, too," he said.
"I will make it over and over.
Then I will make it again."

"Good!" said Sam.

"We like the surprise.

It was a good surprise," he said.

"We will be happy to eat it.

We will eat it again and again."

Vocabulary

The total vocabulary of this book is 66 words, excluding proper names. The 38 words in roman type should be familiar to children reading at a pre-primer level. The 28 words above the pre-primer level are shown in italic type. The number indicates the page on which the word first appears.

after 22	*day* 8	*happy* 7
again 12	did 34	have 13
all 9	down 22	he 11
and 6		*help* 7
are 7	*eat* 9	here 5
away 19		
	find 35	I 8
but 9	for 8	is 5
	fun 17	it 8
	funny 26	
came 8		like 7
can 9		looked 24
come 35	*get* 15	
cowboy 5	go 17	*made* 11
cows 6	good 9	*make* 9